The Waffle Story

How Wendy the Waffle Iron Changed the World

By Natalie Kerrigan
Illustrated by Ray Shilling

A special thanks to our talented
and patient Editors:

Sara Lundy Chorazak
Stefanie Shilling
Dr. Laura Morrison
Dr. Barbara Lundy

The Waffle Story
First Printing November 2010
All Rights Reserved

Published in Hillsboro, Oregon by Innovative Beginnings, LLC
Printed in the USA

ISBN 978-0-615-40699-2

Manufactured by Thomson-Shore, Dexter, MI, USA; RMA 570TB275 November 2010

thewafflestory.com

To The World's Next Great Innovator,

Thank you for adding this book to your collection!

The thought to create a children's version of the Nike Waffle Story was to inspire children to act on their curiosity and to encourage them to think differently.

This story was also written to celebrate Bill Bowerman's life and ensure that his spirit continues to challenge individuals to reach their true potential.

We hope you enjoy the story as much as we have enjoyed putting it together.

Your grateful writer and illustrator,

Natalie and Ray
Nike Employees

I will always remember the first time that I, Wendy the Waffle Iron, saw my new owner.

I had just been polished and was placed on a table in the storefront window. Everyone noticed my perfect shine as they walked by.

I was given the top shelf in my new room and I quickly
made lots of friends.

Bob the Blender told the best jokes and he loved my shiny exterior.

He was always in and out of our room.

Mel the Mixer also lived in our room.

Unlike Bob the Blender, Mel and I were only brought out on Sunday mornings to make the best waffles.

Afterwards, Mrs. Bowerman would carefully clean me so I sparkled and shined before she returned me to my room.

Mrs. Bowerman always said that Mel and I made the best team. We spent our days working together to figure out how to make the most delicious waffles.

Life was going great, until...

... one Sunday morning.

Mel and I tried out a few new waffle-making tricks and made some of our best waffles, if I do say so myself.

Mr. Bowerman, Mrs. Bowerman's husba seemed to especially enjoy them.

After breakfast, instead of being cleaned and put away, Mr. Bowerman picked me up and took me away from the kitchen.

I didn't even get a chance to say goodbye to my friends Mel the Mixer and Bob the Blender.

I was carried out to th[e]
cold and damp garag[e]

Mr. Bowerman then pour[ed]
smelly, heavy goo on m[e]

It was nothing like waffle batte[r]

I did my best to make great waffle[s]
but the goo burned and spilled ov[er]
onto the floor. It was so stick[y]
I could barely open my mout[h]

the end of the day, Mr. Bowerman didn't even clean me! I spent the whole night the cold, damp garage, all dirty with goo stuck to my sides. I wished that I was ck in my room with my friends. I wished that I was clean and shiny again.

Instead, the next day, Mr. Bowerman poured more goo on me. I kept trying and trying to make great waffles, but nothing seemed to work.

The cooked waffle-shaped goo smelled awful, but Mr. Bowerman seemed to be really excited even though I never saw him eat a single, smelly goo-waffle.

I met others in the garage. They were all dirty too, and they were very different than my friends Mel the Mixer and Bob the Blender. They called themselves "tools" and were a little rough around the edges.

Dexter the Drill made loud sounds that scared me. Tom the Tape Measure liked to tell jokes, just like Bob the Blender, but I didn't think Tom's jokes were very funny.

As time went on, I actually became good friends with the tools. Dexter the Drill explained that the smelly goo Mr. Bowerman was pouring on me was rubber. No wonder I couldn't make yummy waffles anymore, and no wonder Mr. Bowerman wasn't eating anything that I made.

But why would he want to make rubber waffles?

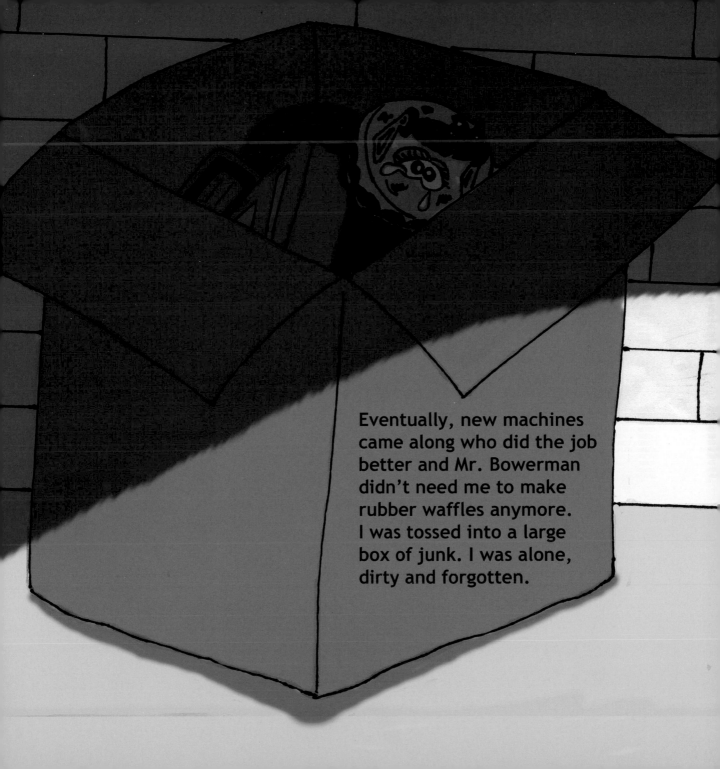

Eventually, new machines came along who did the job better and Mr. Bowerman didn't need me to make rubber waffles anymore. I was tossed into a large box of junk. I was alone, dirty and forgotten.

After many years, I was finally taken out of the box! It turned out that Mr. Bowerman was a great inventor whose curiosity led him to always try new and unusual things.

I, Wendy the Waffle Iron, was one of those crazy ideas that led to a great innovation. Those smelly rubber waffles were the first versions of the Waffle Sole (named after me) and a major improvement in shoes.

Mr. Bowerman had also partnered with Mr. Knight to start a new company to improve the performance of athletes. Through this partnership, the Waffle Sole has been used on millions of shoes to help people all around the world run faster, jump higher and break all sorts of records.

Can you believe it? I thought my life was ruined when Mr. Bowerman took me out to the garage and away from my friends. Instead, it turned out that I was meant to do more than just make delicious, edible waffles.

I was part of a revolution!

Look at me now! I am back on display! Instead of in a storefront, I live in a museum at Nike's World Headquarters. Through all of this, I learned that it doesn't matter how I look. You see, I am still dirty but I am admired more than ever for what I achieved. Even better, my story helps encourage people to think differently and come up with great ideas!

And let me tell you, I have never shined this bright!

"The greatest thing a waffle iron ever did was something it wasn't supposed to"

- Nike's Inspire Innovation Video

Nike's World Headquarters in Beaverton, Oregon

The Steve Prefontaine Building
Home of The Waffle Iron

The Actual Waffle Iron Display

About the Author

Natalie Kerrigan and Barbara Bowerman
February 2010

Natalie Kerrigan pursued a job at Nike in 2001 to match her profession with her personal interest in Health and Fitness. Years later, she continues to work for the company due to her belief that Nike prepares our youth for a successful future by the life lessons they learn through sports.

The story of the Waffle Sole is used throughout Nike as a source of inspiration to motivate Nike employees to continuously innovate and challenge themselves to think differently. The idea to turn this story into a children's book was to bring this same inspiration to children and another way for Natalie to help prepare our youth for a successful future.

Natalie's greatest passion is enjoying the Northwest with her husband, twin boys and daughter.

About the Illustrator

Ray Shilling and Barbara Bowerman
February 2010

Ray Shilling has been working at Nike since 1999. He has always had a love for sports and Nike was the perfect match to bring sports to the work environment. Ever since he was a small child, he has enjoyed spending his spare time drawing. This book was a great opportunity to use his love for drawing and interest in Nike history to help bring The Waffle Story to life.

Ray is a native Oregonian and most enjoys spending time with his wife and two children.

A portion of the proceeds from this book will go to the American Cancer Society and to the Haven House Retirement Center in Fossil, Oregon.